This book belongs to:

....

A NEW BURLINGTON BOOK
The Old Brewery
6 Blundell Street
London N7 9BH

Consultant: Barbara Taylor
Editor: Lauren Taylor
Designer: Elaine Wilkinson

First published in the UK in 2012 by
QED Publishing
A Quarto Group company
230 City Road
London EC1V 2TT

www.qed-publishing.co.uk

A catalogue record for this book is available from the British Library.

ISBN 978 1 78171 015 9

Printed in China

Squirrel's Autumn Search

Anita Loughrey
and Daniel Howarth

NEW
BURLINGTON
BOOKS

Squirrel and his little brother were busy
collecting pine cones, berries and nuts.

Autumn had arrived and food was everywhere.

Juicy blackberries speckled
the thorny brambles.

Corn was being
harvested in the
cornfield.

Squirrel's little brother picked up
one of Squirrel's nuts.
"I bet you can't catch me!" he laughed,
and then he ran away.

They chased each other round in circles.
Colourful leaves swirled all around
and made Squirrel dizzy.

Squirrel chased his little
brother into the woods.

But soon he realized he could
not see his little brother
or his food anywhere.

Squirrel hoped his little
brother wasn't taking
any more of his nuts!

Mouse scampered out of the leaves
carrying a sycamore seed.

Squirrel started to feel hungry.

Squirrel had so enjoyed chasing
his brother that he had forgotten
where he had put his food.

"Have you seen my food?" Squirrel asked Mouse.
"Have you looked in the meadow?" asked Mouse.

Squirrel searched the long
grass in the meadow.
He tutted and scratched his head.

"I'm sure my food was around here somewhere," he said.

Rabbit poked his head
out of his warren to see what
all the noise was about.

"Have you seen my food anywhere?"
asked Squirrel.

"Have you looked by the pond?"
suggested Rabbit.

Squirrel searched through the reeds by the pond.
Leaves were floating on the surface of the water.
Squirrel sniffed the air and tutted.

"I'm sure I buried my food around here somewhere," he said.

Owl was watching Squirrel from above. "Isn't that your little brother over there by the old apple tree?" she asked.

"It looks as if he's got some tasty food to eat!"
said Owl.

Squirrel ran as fast as he could to the apple tree.

Squirrel's little brother was so surprised
that he dropped the nut he was holding.

"I'm sorry," he said. "I was just so hungry."

"Did you know," said Squirrel,
"that food tastes even better if you share it?"

They smiled at each other
and ate their tasty food together.

Autumn activities

Fun and simple ideas for you and
your child to explore together.

What food is harvested in the autumn?
Lots of different types of food are available
for picking and harvesting during autumn.
What types of food are harvested where
you live? Name the foods that
appear in the story.

Go for an autumn walk. The autumn is a great
time for a walk. The weather isn't too hot or
too cold, and it's fun to play in the leaves.
It's also a good time to collect pine cones
and leaves for home craft projects. On
your walk, collect as many different
coloured leaves as you can.

Make a leaf collage. Use the leaves you collected from your autumn walk. For best results, make sure the leaves are completely dry before using them. You can glue them onto card in any pattern you like. Why not also show your child how to do leaf rubbings with wax crayons?

Act out the story with your child. Use paper, pens, pencils and paints to make masks of Squirrel and his friends. Can your child remember anything the characters said? Does your child want to act out the story as it is in the book, or do they want to change the story in their own way?

What did we learn about autumn?

The woods and fields are full of food. Autumn is a season when there is plenty of food, such as berries and nuts. Animals eat as much as they can to build up stores of body fat. They use this fat to help them keep warm in the winter.

Squirrel and his little brother are collecting food. Some animals store food in the autumn. They bury the food in the soil, or hide it away inside holes. They go back to these hiding places to eat the food during the winter.

Corn is being harvested in the cornfield. Autumn is a busy time of year for farmers. They harvest the crops growing in the fields or on fruit trees, and start planting new crops for the following year.

Squirrel chases his little brother in the colourful, falling leaves. As the autumn days get colder, the leaves on some trees turn different shades of red, brown and yellow. This is because the green colour in the leaves breaks down so we can see the other colours hidden underneath. Autumn winds blow the dry leaves off the trees.

Geese are flying over the woods. In the autumn, some birds go on a long migration journey to spend the winter in a warmer place, such as Africa. They will return to their home country when the weather warms up in the spring.